It's Elementary!

Reasoning, Estimating, and Rounding

A Companion to *It's Elementary! 275 Math Word Problems*

M. J. Owen

Educators Publishing Service, Inc.
Cambridge and Toronto

To Ellie, my daughter, with love.

Design by Joyce C. Weston
Illustrations by Tatjana Mai-Wyss

Printed in the U.S.A.

ISBN 0-8388-2414-0

Contents

To the Teacher

Many elementary school students try to solve word problems too quickly or use the wrong operation. In my classroom, I have found it is often an effective strategy to stop after working on a problem and talk about whether the solution is reasonable. This will naturally lead students to question their problem-solving strategies and to check their work independently. This book is designed to improve students' word problem skills with estimation and rounding—in each exercise, students will need to decide whether it is most reasonable to round to the nearest ten, hundred, or thousand. *It's Elementary! Reasoning, Estimating, and Rounding* is a companion volume to *It's Elementary! 275 Math Word Problems* and will be most effective when used with other books in the series.

The problem-solving approach I teach my students is called TINS. The letters in this acronym stand for the different steps students use to analyze and solve word problems. While reading a word problem, students circle key words and note their THOUGHT (T) about the operation they should use to solve the problem. Next they circle and write down the important INFORMATION (I) from the word problem. At this stage I also encourage students to draw a picture of the information and to cross out information that doesn't seem important to the problem. Students then write their information as a NUMBER SENTENCE (N) and plug their answer into a SOLUTION SENTENCE (S). Here's an example:

The Howard family is going to Florida for a vacation. Mrs. Howard paid $101 for her own airline ticket, $103 for Mr. Howard's ticket, and $88 for her daughter Janet's ticket. Estimate how much money it cost for all three people to fly to Florida.

WORK SPACE

Thought (T): +

Information (I): Mom: $101, Dad: $103, Janet: $88

Number Sentence (N): 100 + 100 + 90 =

Solution Sentence (S): It cost about $290 for the Howard family to fly to Florida.

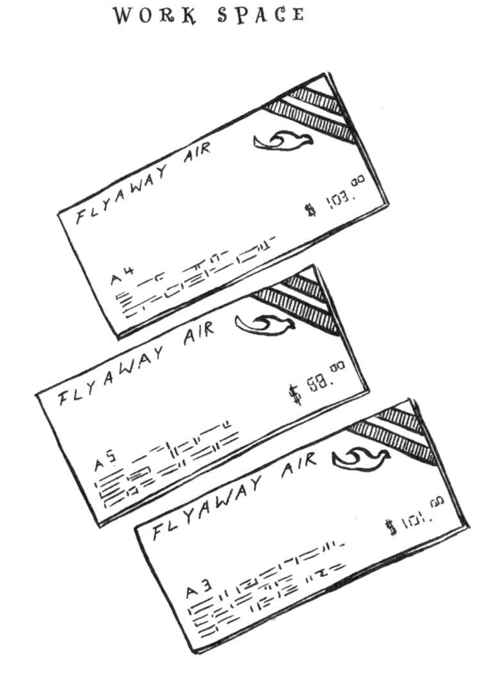

Estimation Skills Review

Round each number as directed.
Remember, 5 or more goes HIGHER; 4 or less goes LOWER!

Round to the nearest ten.

1. 15 ________ **4.** 78 ________ **7.** 31 ________

2. 50 ________ **5.** 82 ________ **8.** 21 ________

3. 119 ________ **6.** 114 ________ **9.** 215 ________

Round to the nearest hundred.

10. 555 ________ **13.** 421 ________ **16.** 788 ________

11. 101 ________ **14.** 875 ________ **17.** 900 ________

12. 450 ________ **15.** 240 ________ **18.** 280 ________

Round to the nearest thousand.

19. 9,001 ________ **22.** 4,100 ________ **25.** 3,000 ________

20. 6,500 ________ **23.** 8,768 ________ **26.** 1,150 ________

21. 3,988 ________ **24.** 4,442 ________ **27.** 4,618 ________

28. Farmer Wiley raises livestock. She has 246 sheep and 115 goats living on her farm. She later adds 145 more sheep to her flock. About how many sheep does farmer Wiley have altogether?

WORK SPACE

Thought: +

Information Sentence: 246 sheep, 145 more sheep

Number Sentence: 200 + 100 =

Solution Sentence: I estimate that Farmer Wiley has 300 sheep altogether.

Does the estimate above seem reasonable to you? How would you have solved this problem? Explain your reasoning.

---

29. Mateo opened a convenience store in his neighborhood. He had 1,212 customers the first week he was in business and 2,033 customers the second week he was in business. About how many more customers did Mateo have in his store during the second week than he had during the first week?

WORK SPACE

Thought: –

Information: 1st week: 1,212, 2nd week: 2,033

Number Sentence: 2,030 – 1,210 =

Solution Sentence: There were about 780 more customers in Mateo's store during the second week.

Does the estimate above seem reasonable to you? How would you have solved this problem? Explain your reasoning.

Estimating Addition Word Problems with TINS

When you read a word problem, think of yourself as an archaeologist. Use the key words as clues to help you uncover the best solution. When you see an addition key word in a problem, circle it and write + above the key word. Then write + on the THOUGHT line. Next, circle and write down the important INFORMATION from the word problem. Sometimes it helps to draw a picture of the important information. It's also a good idea to cross out information that doesn't seem important to the problem. Now write a NUMBER SENTENCE with your estimated or rounded information. Then plug your estimate into your SOLUTION SENTENCE.

Here are some addition key words. If you know other addition words, add them to this list.

- add (and added)
- altogether
- in all
- together
- total
- sum

Remember, you will need to estimate, or round, your answers. When you see an estimation key word, it means that the problem is looking for the most reasonable estimate and not an exact answer. Here are some estimation key words to look for.

- about
- estimate
- a good estimate

Don't forget that 5 or more goes HIGHER; 4 or less goes LOWER! In the beginning, it might help to write this above each problem.

Example: Mr. Hartman brought 3 items home from the grocery store. Each item costs between \$2.40 and \$1.82. What is a good estimate of how much money Mr. Hartman spent on groceries altogether?

Thought (T): +

Information (I): 3 items, between \$ 2.40 and \$1.82

Number Sentence (N): 2 + 2 + 2 =

Solution Sentence (S): Mr. Hartman spent about \$6 on groceries.

WORK SPACE

A good way to remember how to solve word problems is to think of the word TINS.

T = Thought

I = Information

N = Number Sentence

S = Solution Sentence

Round reasonably and enjoy estimating!

Try It Out

Use TINS to estimate the solutions to these addition word problems. Remember to circle key words, draw pictures, and cross out extra information. The first 2 problems have pictures to help you.

1. Julienne spent $43.55 on a new dress, $31.09 on a pair of shoes, and $10.88 on lunch. About how much money did Julienne spend on her shoes and her new dress?

WORK SPACE

Thought: ____________________

Information: ____________________

____

Number Sentence: $43.55 + $31.09

Solution Sentence: She spent about $75.00

31.09
41

---

2. Janeese has 18 dolls in her doll collection. When her sister Anna went away to college she gave Janeese 17 more dolls. Can you estimate the number of dolls that are in Janeese's doll collection now?

WORK SPACE

T: +

I: ____________________

____

N: 18 + 17 =

S: She now has 35 dolls

____

3. During the holidays, Nicole spent $24 on a gift for her brother, $16 on a gift for her sister, and $32 on a gift for her mom. About how much money did Nicole spend on all three gifts?

WORK SPACE

T: ______________________________

I: ______________________________

____

N: ______________________________

S: ______________________________

____

4. Gregory bought 48 basketball cards, 23 football cards, and 19 baseball cards. Estimate the sum of baseball and basketball cards that Gregory bought in all.

WORK SPACE

T: ______________________________

I: ______________________________

____

N: ______________________________

S: ______________________________

____

5. Kai went on vacation. She spent between $6.11 and $10.91 on each of her three meals. About how much money did Kai spend on the three meals in total?

WORK SPACE

T: ______________________________

I: ______________________________

____

N: ______________________________

S: ______________________________

____

6. Marty found there were 289 tadpoles at Foster Pond and 387 tadpoles at Versailles Pond. What is a good estimate of how many tadpoles Marty found in all?

WORK SPACE

T: ______________________________

I: ______________________________

____

N: ______________________________

S: ______________________________

____

7. Danielle drove 323 miles on Saturday and 123 miles on Sunday. About how many miles did Danielle drive on both days?

WORK SPACE

T: ______________________________

I: ______________________________

____

N: ______________________________

S: ______________________________

____

8. Jose is training for the Vancouver marathon. The marathon is 26.2 miles long. During Jose's tenth week of training, he runs 54 miles. During the eleventh week, he runs 64 miles. During the twelfth week, he runs 68. Estimate the number of miles Jose runs during weeks ten, eleven, and twelve.

WORK SPACE

T: ______________________________

I: ______________________________

____

N: ______________________________

S: ______________________________

____

9. Marcy saved money all summer working as a lifeguard. In June she earned $349.02, in July she earned $490.11, and in August she earned $202.34. Marcy wants to buy a computer that costs $800. Estimate the sum of Marcy's earnings all summer.

WORK SPACE

T: ______________________________

I: ______________________________

____

N: ______________________________

S: ______________________________

____

---

10. Honora has $10 to spend on groceries. She wants to buy shampoo that costs $3.89, a dozen eggs for $1.69, and a loaf of bread that costs $1.02. About how much money will Honora spend on groceries?

WORK SPACE

T: ______________________________

I: ______________________________

____

N: ______________________________

S: ______________________________

____

Estimating Subtraction Word Problems with TINS

You can use TINS to estimate subtraction word problems, too! Think of yourself as a game show contestant—identify the key words to find the best answer first. When you see a subtraction key word in a problem, circle it and write – above the key word. Then write – on the THOUGHT line. Next, circle and write down the important INFORMATION from the word problem. Sometimes it helps to draw a picture of the important information and cross out information that doesn't seem important to the problem. Now write the important information as a NUMBER SENTENCE. Then plug your estimates into your SOLUTION SENTENCE. Here are some subtraction key words. Can you think of any others? If so, add them to this list.

- difference
- left
- subtract
- how many more
- how much more

Check out this example problem:

Example: Sharon bought 14 balloons and ~~5 pizza pies~~ for her party. On the way home from the store, she heard between 1 and 3 balloons pop. How many balloons were left for the party?

Thought: –

Information: 14 balloons, between 1 and 3 popped

Number Sentence: 14 – 2 =

Solution Sentence: There were about eleven balloons for the party.

WORK SPACE

Try It Out

Use TINS to estimate the solutions to these subtraction word problems. Remember to circle key words, draw pictures, and cross out extra information. The first 2 problems have pictures to help you.

1. David has to read a book that is 543 pages long. If he has 401 pages left to read, about how many pages has he already completed?

WORK SPACE

I 401 Pages

Thought: ______________________________

Information: ______________________________

____

Number Sentence: ______________________________

Solution Sentence: ______________________________

____

---

2. John stopped on the street corner to buy 18 tulips for his sister. On his way home, he noticed that between 2 and 4 flowers had already begun opening. How many tulips had not opened yet?

WORK SPACE

T: ______________________________

I: ______________________________

____

N: ______________________________

S: ______________________________

____

3. 767 students attend McRidge Junior High School. Every day between 232 and 289 students ride the bus to school. Estimate how many students do not ride the bus to school every day.

WORK SPACE

T: ______________________________

I: ______________________________

____

N: ______________________________

S: ______________________________

____

4. Leila spent $187 on groceries in October and $101 on groceries in November. About how much more did Leila spend on groceries in October?

WORK SPACE

T: ______________________________

I: ______________________________

____

N: ______________________________

S: ______________________________

____

5. Johanna bakes 127 apple turnovers for the bake sale. She sells 74 of them. About how many turnovers does she have left?

WORK SPACE

T: ______________________________

I: ______________________________

____

N: ______________________________

S: ______________________________

____

6. During last year's baseball season, 231 baseball games were scheduled at Marigold Park. 41 games were rained out and not rescheduled. Give the best estimate for the number of baseball games played at Marigold Park last season.

WORK SPACE

T: ______________________________

I: ______________________________

____

N: ______________________________

S: ______________________________

____

7. Molly pays $323 to fly to New York City. Rebecca pays $417 to fly to New York City. Estimate the difference in cost between Rebecca's flight and Molly's flight.

WORK SPACE

T: ______________________________

I: ______________________________

____

N: ______________________________

S: ______________________________

____

---

8. Margot deposits $122 into her savings account in the fall and $211 in the spring. About how much more money does Margot deposit in the spring?

WORK SPACE

T: ______________________________

I: ______________________________

____

N: ______________________________

S: ______________________________

____

9. There are 898 students enrolled at Blue Lake Elementary. There are 322 students enrolled at Pleasant Hills Elementary. About how many more students are enrolled at Blue Lake Elementary?

WORK SPACE

T: ______________________________

I: ______________________________

____

N: ______________________________

S: ______________________________

____

10. There are 619 streetlights in a neighborhood of downtown Atlanta. Between 289 and 306 streetlights will need replacement bulbs soon. What is a good estimate of how many streetlights will need new bulbs?

WORK SPACE

T: ______________________________

I: ______________________________

____

N: ______________________________

S: ______________________________

____

On Your Own

Use TINS to solve these word problems. Remember to circle key words, draw pictures, and cross out extra information.

1. Joey saves $445 over summer vacation. Peter saves $111 over summer vacation. About how much more money did Joey save over summer vacation?

WORK SPACE

Thought: ______________________________

Information: ______________________________

____

Number Sentence: ______________________________

Solution Sentence: ______________________________

____

---

2. Three girls have marble collections. Elizabeth has 335 marbles, Shannah has 432 marbles, and Luisa has 613 marbles. What is a good estimate of how many marbles Shannah and Luisa have altogether?

WORK SPACE

T: ______________________________

I: ______________________________

____

N: ______________________________

S: ______________________________

____

3. During the month of June, Alaska Whitewater Adventures took 787 people whitewater rafting. In July, the same company took 999 people whitewater rafting. About how many people did Alaska Whitewater Adventures take rafting in June and July?

WORK SPACE

T: ______________________________

I: ______________________________

____

N: ______________________________

S: ______________________________

____

4. Lee has $187. He spends $98 on a new bicycle. About how much money does Lee have left?

WORK SPACE

T: ______________________________

I: ______________________________

____

N: ______________________________

S: ______________________________

____

5. Marissa's summer school class goes on field trips three days a week. On Monday, they drive 100 miles to the San Antonio zoo. On Wednesday, they drive 33 miles to a state park. On Friday, they drive 117 miles to a museum in Houston. About how many more miles did Marissa's summer school class drive on Friday than on Wednesday?

WORK SPACE

T: ______________________________

I: ______________________________

____

N: ______________________________

S: ______________________________

____

6. There are 317 campers who attend Exploration Day Camp in June and 122 campers who attend in August. Estimate how many more campers attend Exploration in June?

WORK SPACE

T: ______________________________

I: ______________________________

____

N: ______________________________

S: ______________________________

____

7. Deepal collects baseball cards. She collected 276 cards when she was in sixth grade and 654 cards when she was in seventh grade. About how many baseball cards did she collect altogether?

WORK SPACE

T: ______________________________

I: ______________________________

____

N: ______________________________

S: ______________________________

____

8. In New Mexico, the temperature was 100 degrees for 22 days in June and for 28 days in July. Estimate how many more 100-degree days there were in New Mexico in July than there were in June.

WORK SPACE

T: ______________________________

I: ______________________________

____

N: ______________________________

S: ______________________________

____

9. Oliver climbed 18 trees in November and 27 trees in December. Estimate the number of trees Oliver climbed altogether.

WORK SPACE

T: ____________________

I: ____________________

____

N: ____________________

S: ____________________

____

10. The cafeteria can hold a maximum of 877 people. The auditorium can hold a maximum of 433 people. About how many more people can the cafeteria hold than the auditorium?

WORK SPACE

T: ____________________

I: ____________________

____

N: ____________________

S: ____________________

____

Estimating Addition and Subtraction: Take the Challenge

Make a list of the addition key words you know.

____

____

____

____

____

____

Make a list of the subtraction key words you know.

____

____

____

____

____

____

Remember to look for and circle these words in the problems below. Draw pictures, cross out extra information, and use TINS to estimate the best answer. Think about your solution sentence. Does it seem reasonable?

---

1. Bonnie's ferry was scheduled to arrive at Bridgeport at 12:12 P.M. but was between 35 and 45 minutes late. About what time did Bonnie finally arrive?

WORK SPACE

Thought: ______________________________

Information: ______________________________

____

Number Sentence: ______________________________

Solution Sentence: ______________________________

____

2. Mr. Singh goes to the farmer's market on Saturday and Sunday. On Saturday he spends $67.75 on fresh fruits and on Sunday he spends $34.50 on fresh vegetables. Estimate the difference in cost for Mr. Singh's fruits and vegetables.

WORK SPACE

T: ______________________________

I: ______________________________

____

N: ______________________________

S: ______________________________

____

---

3. Sal volunteers at the children's hospital 16 hours each week. If he volunteers 8 hours each week at the library, about how many hours does he volunteer in one week?

WORK SPACE

T: ______________________________

I: ______________________________

____

N: ______________________________

S: ______________________________

____

---

4. During the fall, Principal Baker sold carnival tickets for the Hillside School Carnival. He sold 3,456 tickets during September and 1,998 tickets during October. About how many more tickets did he sell during September?

WORK SPACE

T: ______________________________

I: ______________________________

____

N: ______________________________

S: ______________________________

____

5. The library bookshelves hold 2,111 fifth-grade books, 1,234 sixth-grade books, and 1,988 seventh-grade books. What is a good estimate of the total number of books the library has for students in grades five through seven?

WORK SPACE

T: ______________________________

I: ______________________________

____

N: ______________________________

S: ______________________________

____

---

6. The distance between the city of Austin and the city of Houston is 180 miles. Wyatt drives from Houston to his grandparents' house in Austin and then back home to Houston. About how many miles does Wyatt travel in sum?

WORK SPACE

T: ______________________________

I: ______________________________

____

N: ______________________________

S: ______________________________

____

---

7. Aunt Giselle spends $289.00 on four birthday presents for her nieces. Uncle Frank spends $345.98 on four birthday gifts for his nieces. Estimate how much more money Uncle Frank spends.

WORK SPACE

T: ______________________________

I: ______________________________

____

N: ______________________________

S: ______________________________

____

8. Kin spends thirty-five minutes on his homework on Monday and Tuesday, 45 minutes on Wednesday, and 55 minutes on Thursday and Friday. Estimate how many minutes Kin spends on his homework for the entire week.

WORK SPACE

T: ____________________

I: ____________________

____

N: ____________________

S: ____________________

____

9. Linquist Elementary is having a bake sale. The school earned $397 from selling baked goods but had already spent $44 on advertising and supplies. About how much money does Linquist Elementary make from the bake sale?

WORK SPACE

T: ____________________

I: ____________________

____

N: ____________________

S: ____________________

____

10. Samantha and Timothy volunteered to help clean up their neighborhood park. Samantha picked up 321 pieces of trash. Timothy picked up 234 pieces of trash. Estimate how many pieces of trash Samantha and Timothy picked up together.

WORK SPACE

T: ____________________

I: ____________________

____

N: ____________________

S: ____________________

____

11. The Nisimblats traveled 733 miles by train on Saturday and 345 miles by car on Sunday. About how many more miles did they travel on Saturday?

WORK SPACE

T: ______

I: ______

______

N: ______

S: ______

______

12. Julia owns a concession stand. She sells 76 sandwiches, 44 pretzels, 100 drinks, and 23 bags of peanuts at the football game. What is a good estimate of the total number of items Julia sold at the game?

WORK SPACE

T: ______

I: ______

______

N: ______

S: ______

______

13. Sasha saved $50.00 from baby-sitting over spring break. She spent $17.50 at the bookstore. About how much money does Sasha have left?

WORK SPACE

T: ______

I: ______

______

N: ______

S: ______

______

14. Will's family went to a concert over the weekend. His mom's ticket and his dad's ticket cost $33.00 each. Will's ticket cost $15.75, and his little sister's ticket cost $14.00. Estimate how much it cost for Will's whole family to go to the concert.

WORK SPACE

T: ______________________________

I: ______________________________

____

N: ______________________________

S: ______________________________

____

---

15. Baty Elementary raised $13,765.98 by sponsoring a community carnival. If the school spent $543.98 on carnival prizes, about how much money did Batey Elementary raise?

WORK SPACE

T: ______________________________

I: ______________________________

____

N: ______________________________

S: ______________________________

____

---

16. The University of Washington bookstore employs 97 students. Twenty-one of these students are freshmen and the rest are seniors. Estimate how many seniors work at the bookstore.

WORK SPACE

T: ______________________________

I: ______________________________

____

N: ______________________________

S: ______________________________

____

17. During a 72-hour period, Lane sleeps 23 hours. Estimate the number of hours that Lane is awake.

WORK SPACE

T: ____________________

I: ____________________

____

N: ____________________

S: ____________________

____

---

18. Marcus delivers pizza during the summer. Last June he delivered 2,998 pizzas; last July he delivered 1,234 pizzas; and last August he delivered 2,345 pizzas. What is a good estimate of the total number of pizzas Marcus delivered during last summer?

WORK SPACE

T: ____________________

I: ____________________

____

N: ____________________

S: ____________________

____

---

19. Three roommates went to the grocery store. Lindsey spent $39.77, Nadia spent $54.34, and Lita spent $45.08. About how much money did the three girls spend altogether?

WORK SPACE

T: ____________________

I: ____________________

____

N: ____________________

S: ____________________

____

20. Jeremy has 172 CDs in his music collection. Malcolm has 278 CDs in his collection. Jeremy receives 4 new CDs for his birthday. What is a good estimate for the sum of the boys' CDs?

WORK SPACE

T: ______________________________

I: ______________________________

____

N: ______________________________

S: ______________________________

____

Write Your Own I

Use the information provided to write your own addition or subtraction word problems. Then use TINS to solve each one. Check that your answers seem reasonable. Challenge your friends to estimate the best solution to some of the problems you've written!

WORK SPACE

Example: Eighteen classmates and twelve teammates were invited.

Question: Dan invited 18 classmates and 12 baseball teammates to his birthday party. About how many people did Dan invite in all?

Thought: +

Information: 18 classmates, 12 teammates

Number Sentence: 20 + 10 =

Solution Sentence: Dan invited about 30 people to his party.

WORK SPACE

1. The Wright brothers' first plane, Flyer I, weighed between 720 and 750 pounds. Its 12-horsepower engine weighed between 160 and 180 pounds.

Question: ______________________________

____

______________________________?

Thought: ______________________________

Information: ______________________________

Number Sentence: ______________________________

Solution Sentence: ______________________________

____

2. Sequoyah has $243. Maria has $117.

WORK SPACE

Question: ______________________________

____

______________________________?

T: ______________________________

I: ______________________________

____

N: ______________________________

S: ______________________________

____

3. There are 18 toboggan slopes in all. Eight of the slopes are used for first-time tobogganers.

WORK SPACE

Question: ______________________________

____

______________________________?

T: ______________________________

I: ______________________________

____

N: ______________________________

S: ______________________________

____

4. Martin makes $25.00 mowing the yard. He later earns $16.00.

WORK SPACE

Question: ______________________________

____

______________________________?

T: ______________________________

I: ______________________________

____

N: ______________________________

S: ______________________________

____

---

5. Ms. Iyer wrote 25 computer programs. She sold 8 of them.

WORK SPACE

Question: ______________________________

____

______________________________?

T: ______________________________

I: ______________________________

____

N: ______________________________

S: ______________________________

____

Write Your Own II

Write five new addition and subtraction word problems using your own information. Remember to draw a picture, circle key words, and cross out extra information for each problem. Then use TINS to estimate a reasonable solution. Be creative!

1. ____

____

____?

T: ____

I: ____

____

N: ____

S: ____

____

WORK SPACE

---

2. ____

____

____?

T: ____

I: ____

____

N: ____

S: ____

____

WORK SPACE

3. ____________________

____

____________________?

T: ____________________

I: ____________________

____

N: ____________________

S: ____________________

____

WORK SPACE

4. ____________________

____

____________________?

T: ____________________

I: ____________________

____

N: ____________________

S: ____________________

____

WORK SPACE

5. ____________________

____

____________________?

T: ____________________

I: ____________________

____

N: ____________________

S: ____________________

____

WORK SPACE

Addition and Subtraction Mixed Review

Use TINS to solve these word problems. Remember to circle key words, draw pictures, and cross out extra information. Check that your solutions are reasonable.

1. Savannah has a collection of miniature dollhouse pieces. She has 798 pieces in her collection. Nelie gives her 17 new pieces and 4 barrettes for her birthday. What is a good estimate of how many miniature dollhouse pieces Savannah has now?

WORK SPACE

Thought: ______________________________

Information: ______________________________

____

Number Sentence: ______________________________

Solution Sentence: ______________________________

____

2. Jeffrey saved $56.80 in fourth grade and $34.50 in fifth grade. What is a good estimate of how much money Jeffrey saved during fourth and fifth grade?

WORK SPACE

T: ______________________________

I: ______________________________

____

N: ______________________________

S: ______________________________

____

3. Trudy and Lovett are captains of the swim team. They swim 19 miles the first week of practice, 22 miles the second week, and 41 miles the third week. What is a good estimate of the total number of miles Trudy and Lovett swim in three weeks?

WORK SPACE

T: ______________________________

I: ______________________________

____

N: ______________________________

S: ______________________________

____

4. Desiree's family drove 589 miles on the first day of vacation and 543 miles on the second day of vacation. About how many more miles did Desiree's family drive on the first day of vacation?

WORK SPACE

T: ______________________________

I: ______________________________

____

N: ______________________________

S: ______________________________

____

5. Jaime learns to play 12 new songs during the first two weeks of his piano lessons and 18 new songs during his third and fourth weeks of lessons. About how many songs can Jaime play after four weeks of piano lessons?

WORK SPACE

T: ______________________________

I: ______________________________

____

N: ______________________________

S: ______________________________

____

6. Mr. Cardwell starts out the school year with 5,897 pieces of notebook paper. After the first semester, he still has 789 pieces of paper. About how many pieces of notebook paper did Mr. Cardwell use during the first semester?

WORK SPACE

T: ______________________________

I: ______________________________

____

N: ______________________________

S: ______________________________

____

7. The circus sold 1,001 tickets for its first performance and 945 tickets for its second performance. About how many more people attended the first performance?

WORK SPACE

T: ______________________________

I: ______________________________

____

N: ______________________________

S: ______________________________

____

8. The elementary school in Westville has 675 students; the middle school has 786 students; and the high school has 998 students. Estimate the total number of students enrolled in all three Westville schools.

WORK SPACE

T: ______________________________

I: ______________________________

____

N: ______________________________

S: ______________________________

____

9. Terrance's geometry book has 976 pages. He completed 543 of these pages before his vacation. About how many pages of work will Terrance have left to complete after his vacation?

WORK SPACE

T: ____________________

I: ____________________

____

N: ____________________

S: ____________________

____

---

10. Theresa's family is taking the train to Chicago. It cost $99 for Theresa's ticket, $172 for her mom's ticket, and $101 for her Aunt Bethany's ticket. Estimate how much the three train tickets cost in all.

WORK SPACE

T: ____________________

I: ____________________

____

N: ____________________

S: ____________________

____

---

11. The Big Screen movie theater sold 1,040 tickets on Saturday night and 1,298 tickets on Sunday night. About how many tickets did The Big Screen sell on both nights?

WORK SPACE

T: ____________________

I: ____________________

____

N: ____________________

S: ____________________

____

12. Molly is in a play at The University of Virginia. The university sold 7,688 tickets for Friday night's performance, 8,787 tickets for Saturday's night performance, and 8,190 for Sunday night's performance. About how many more tickets did the play sell for Sunday night than for Friday night?

WORK SPACE

T: ______________________________

I: ______________________________

____

N: ______________________________

S: ______________________________

____

13. Tyree's marching band is traveling to California to play in a famous parade. They travel 1,198 miles to get there and they travel the same distance to return home. About how many miles does Tyree's band travel in all?

WORK SPACE

T: ______________________________

I: ______________________________

____

N: ______________________________

S: ______________________________

____

14. Jojo and Miriam went bird watching. They counted 3,432 birds on Monday morning and 4,339 birds on Tuesday morning. What is a good estimate of the total number of birds Jojo and Miriam counted together?

WORK SPACE

T: ______________________________

I: ______________________________

____

N: ______________________________

S: ______________________________

____

15. Pat and Tara are planning to send Valentine's Day cards to friends and relatives who live out of town. They spend $29 on cards and $14 on stamps. About how much do Pat and Tara spend in all?

WORK SPACE

T: ______________________________

I: ______________________________

____

N: ______________________________

S: ______________________________

____

---

16. At the Yankees game, Martina spent $32.00 on souvenirs. Her brother spent $17.00, and her cousin spent $23.45. Estimate the total cost of their souvenirs.

WORK SPACE

T: ______________________________

I: ______________________________

____

N: ______________________________

S: ______________________________

____

---

17. Solomon spent 22 hours landscaping his grandmother's yard during the first weekend of May and 29 hours during the second weekend. Estimate how many hours Solomon spent landscaping during the first two weekends of May.

WORK SPACE

T: ______________________________

I: ______________________________

____

N: ______________________________

S: ______________________________

____

18. Janna has $248. She spends $78 on a new computer monitor. About how much money does Janna have left?

WORK SPACE

T: ____________________

I: ____________________

____

N: ____________________

S: ____________________

____

19. Maxwell starts an exercise journal to keep track of the miles he walks. He walks 23 miles the first week, 35 miles the second week, and 44 miles the third week. What is a good estimate of his total mileage for the three weeks?

WORK SPACE

T: ____________________

I: ____________________

____

N: ____________________

S: ____________________

____

20. Sierra received 19 e-mail messages on Monday and 27 e-mail messages on Tuesday. About how many e-mail messages did Sierra receive altogether?

WORK SPACE

T: ____________________

I: ____________________

____

N: ____________________

S: ____________________

____

Explain

Use TINS to solve each addition or subtraction problem. Then write at least 2 sentences explaining why your estimate is reasonable.

Example: Whitney had $98.75. She spent $36.23 when she went out with her friends. About how much money does Whitney have left?

Thought: –

Information: had $98.75, spent $36.23

Number Sentence: 100 – 36 =

Solution Sentence: Whitney had about $64 left.

Explanation: I chose to round to the nearest ten because $98.75 is very close to $100. I think that with this much money it would not be useful to round to the nearest one dollar or to the nearest cent.

---

1. 1,876 students attend Marvin's school. 1,032 students are going on a field trip on Friday. About how many students will remain at the school?

WORK SPACE

Thought: ____________________

Information: ____________________

Number Sentence: ____________________

Solution Sentence: ____________________

Explanation: ____________________

____

____

____

2. In 1996, Ms. Moreno had 32 students in her class. She had 21 students in 1997, 30 students in 1998, and 29 students in 1999. What is a good estimate of the total number of students Ms. Moreno taught from 1996 through 1999?

WORK SPACE

T: ______________________

I: ______________________

____

N: ______________________

S: ______________________

____

Explanation: ______________________

____

____

____

3. Jack's sister is driving him to his grandparents' farm to spend the summer. They drive 344 miles on Monday, 456 miles on Tuesday, and 102 miles on Wednesday. About how many miles do Jack and his sister drive in all?

WORK SPACE

T: ______________________

I: ______________________

____

N: ______________________

S: ______________________

____

Explanation: ______________________

____

____

____

Estimating Multiplication Word Problems with TINS

Don't let multiplication word problems win. Use the key words to estimate your next best move! When you see a multiplication key word in a problem, circle it and write × above the key word. Then write × on the THOUGHT line. Next, circle and write down the important INFORMATION from the word problem. Sometimes it helps to draw a picture of the important information and cross out information that doesn't seem important. Now write the important information as a NUMBER SENTENCE. Then plug your estimate into your SOLUTION SENTENCE. Below are some key words that appear in multiplication word problems. Do you know any others? If so, add them to the list.

groups (and other words that are kinds of groups)

Examples: *groups* of campers, *batches* of cookies, *bunches* of grapes, *bags* of groceries, *schools* of fish

each *Each* is a tricky key word because it shows up in division problems, too. You'll know you are most likely reading a multiplication problem if *each* shows up with one of its buddies: *altogether, in all,* or *total.*

Example: Latricia spent ~~30 minutes~~ at the supermarket. She bought (5 items.) If the price of the items ranged (from $1.89 to $4.11), what is a good estimate of how much money Latricia spent (in all?)

Thought: ×

Information: 5 items, between $1.89 and $4.11

Number Sentence: 5 × 3 =

Solution Sentence: Latricia spent around $15 on groceries in all.

WORK SPACE

Try It Out

Use TINS to estimate the solutions to these multiplication word problems. Remember to circle key words, draw pictures, and cross out extra information. The first 2 problems have pictures to help you.

1. Astronomers estimate that the planet Saturn is 9.5 times wider than Earth. If Earth is 7,926 miles wide, about how many miles wide is Saturn?

WORK SPACE

Thought: ______________________

Information: ______________________

____

Number Sentence: ______________________

Solution Sentence: ______________________

____

---

2. Penny's cat Marshmallow has 6 rows of whiskers on his face. If each row has between 6 and 8 whiskers, estimate the number of whiskers on Marshmallow's face.

WORK SPACE

T: ______________________

I: ______________________

____

N: ______________________

S: ______________________

____

3. Abigail bought 46 plastic cups for the party. If 16 people use 2 cups each, will Abigail have enough cups for her party?

WORK SPACE

T: ______________________________

I: ______________________________

____

N: ______________________________

S: ______________________________

____

4. Elephants sleep between 1 and 3 hours each day. Chimpanzees and seals nap several times a day. Estimate the number of hours an elephant sleeps in one week.

WORK SPACE

T: ______________________________

I: ______________________________

____

N: ______________________________

S: ______________________________

____

5. While they are sleeping, most people swallow between 6.9 and 7.6 times each hour. If Marta sleeps for 8 hours, about how many times will she swallow?

WORK SPACE

T: ______________________________

I: ______________________________

____

N: ______________________________

S: ______________________________

____

---

6. Vincent sold 20 bags of red pistachios. Each bag contains between 25 and 32 nuts. About how many nuts did Vincent sell in all?

WORK SPACE

T: ______________________________

I: ______________________________

____

N: ______________________________

S: ______________________________

____

7. Baily can type between 58 and 62 words a minute on her computer. About how many words can Baily type in 5 minutes?

WORK SPACE

T: ______________________________

I: ______________________________

____

N: ______________________________

S: ______________________________

____

8. In one minute, a whale's heart will probably have beaten between 8 and 10 times. Estimate how many times a whale's heart will have beaten after 15 minutes.

WORK SPACE

T: ______________________________

I: ______________________________

____

N: ______________________________

S: ______________________________

____

9. Floyd saw 3 schools of bluefish from his boat. Floyd counted at least 55 fish in each school. About how many bluefish were there altogether?

WORK SPACE

T: ______________________________

I: ______________________________

____

N: ______________________________

S: ______________________________

____

10. Angel is studying social psychology. She reports that one person may have 32 conversations in one day. Estimate how many conversations a person may have in one week.

WORK SPACE

T: ______________________________

I: ______________________________

____

N: ______________________________

S: ______________________________

____

Estimating Division Word Problems with TINS

TINS is an important ingredient in addition, subtraction, and multiplication word problems. As you may have guessed, it can help you prepare the correct answers to division problems, too! When you see a division key word in a problem, circle it and write ÷ above the key word. Then write ÷ on the THOUGHT line. Next, circle and write down the important INFORMATION from the word problem. Sometimes it helps to draw a picture of the important information and cross out information that doesn't seem important to the problem. Now write the important information as a NUMBER SENTENCE. Then plug your answer into your SOLUTION SENTENCE. Check out this list of division key words and add other division key words you know.

- each
- equally
- separate
- equal
- divide

Each is that pesky key word that also appears in multiplication word problems. If *each* appears with another division key word, such as *divide* or *equally*, then you are probably dealing with a division problem.

Example: Nine passengers get off the train at Sidestreet Station. Twenty-one people are waiting for the passengers to arrive. Estimate how many people are waiting to greet each passenger.

Thought: ÷

Information: 9 passengers, 21 people waiting

Number Sentence: 20 ÷ 10 =

Solution Sentence: There are about 2 people waiting to greet each passenger.

WORK SPACE

Try It Out

Use TINS to estimate the solutions to these division word problems. Remember to circle key words, draw pictures, and cross out extra information. The first 2 problems have pictures to help you.

1. Wilma hitched 8 Siberian huskies to her dogsled. The total weight of the dogs on her team was 586 pounds. Estimate the weight of each dog on Wilma's team.

WORK SPACE

Thought: ______________________________

Information: ______________________________

____

Number Sentence: ______________________________

Solution Sentence: ______________________________

____

---

2. Camp Rivercloud wants to set up 9 new tents. Between 22 and 31 campers will be available to help. About how many campers will be working on each tent?

WORK SPACE

T: ______________________________

I: ______________________________

____

N: ______________________________

S: ______________________________

____

3. An offshore oil-drilling platform weighs between 45,500 and 47,900 tons. This is 4 times more than the weight of the Eiffel Tower. About how heavy is the Eiffel Tower?

WORK SPACE

T: ______________________________

I: ______________________________

____

N: ______________________________

S: ______________________________

____

4. Nelson Baxter is a professional wallpaper hanger. It took him 26 hours to hang paper on 55 walls. Nelson gives each new client a 10% discount. About how many hours did Nelson Baxter spend on each wall?

WORK SPACE

T: ______________________________

I: ______________________________

____

N: ______________________________

S: ______________________________

____

5. Mr. Pardo planted 56 tomato plants. His plants produced between 3,000 and 3,400 cherry tomatoes. About how many tomatoes did Mr. Pardo pick from each plant?

WORK SPACE

T: ______________________________

I: ______________________________

____

N: ______________________________

S: ______________________________

____

---

6. Grandfather Lindholm slept a total of 27 hours in 3 nights. Estimate the number of hours Grandfather Lindholm slept each night.

WORK SPACE

T: ______________________________

I: ______________________________

____

N: ______________________________

S: ______________________________

____

7. Grandma Pilicy keeps photos in 5 albums. In each of her albums she has about the same number of photos. If she has a total of 871 photos, what is a good estimate of the number of photos in each of her albums?

WORK SPACE

T: ______________________________

I: ______________________________

____

N: ______________________________

S: ______________________________

____

8. Mr. Tablett has 425 tickets to sell for the museum's Egyptian hieroglyphics exhibit. Mr. Tablett wants to sell all of the tickets in 18 days. About how many tickets will he need to sell each day?

WORK SPACE

T: ______________________________

I: ______________________________

____

N: ______________________________

S: ______________________________

____

9. Ada Crumpet's bakery uses 52 pounds of unsalted butter in her pastries each day. Ada knows that she has 680 pounds of butter left in her freezer. If she divides her supply equally, about how many days will Ada's butter last?

WORK SPACE

T: ______________________________

I: ______________________________

____

N: ______________________________

S: ______________________________

____

10. By the end of the day, Walter had waited on 22 customers at his restaurant. If Walter made $35.55 in tips, about how much did he receive from each customer?

WORK SPACE

T: ______________________________

I: ______________________________

____

N: ______________________________

S: ______________________________

____

On Your Own

Use TINS to solve these multiplication and division word problems.
Remember to circle key words, draw pictures, and cross out extra information.

1. Elmer bought 30 shares of stock in a toy company. The value of each share fluctuates between $58 and $63. Estimate the total value of Elmer's stocks.

WORK SPACE

Thought: ______________________________

Information: ______________________________

____

Number Sentence: ______________________________

Solution Sentence: ______________________________

____

---

2. Over the summer, Olive sold 35 beaded bracelets at the Moosehead Lake craft fair. If Olive made $589.25 at the fair, about how much did she charge for each bracelet?

WORK SPACE

T: ______________________________

I: ______________________________

____

N: ______________________________

S: ______________________________

____

3. Detective Case found 25 clues in 3 rooms at the crime scene. If the separate rooms had about the same number of clues, how many clues were found in each room?

WORK SPACE

T: ____________________

I: ____________________

____

N: ____________________

S: ____________________

____

4. Pearl spends between 110 and 120 minutes traveling on the bus to and from school every day. Estimate how many minutes Pearl spends on the school bus in 5 days.

WORK SPACE

T: ____________________

I: ____________________

____

N: ____________________

S: ____________________

____

5. A full-grown sea manatee is 16 feet long. In one day a manatee can eat 98 pounds of seagrass. About how many pounds of seagrass can a manatee eat in one week?

WORK SPACE

T: ______________________________

I: ______________________________

____

N: ______________________________

S: ______________________________

____

6. Doris Hemple flew her small plane over the Potomac River. Ms. Hemple used 26 gallons of fuel in one hour. Estimate how many gallons of fuel Ms. Hemple will use if she flies her plane for 3 hours.

WORK SPACE

T: ______________________________

I: ______________________________

____

N: ______________________________

S: ______________________________

____

7. Arnold Bulfinch raised 51 chickens that weigh a total of 158 pounds altogether. A typical hen can lay between 220 and 227 eggs in one year. Estimate the weight in pounds of each of his chickens.

WORK SPACE

T: ______________________________

I: ______________________________

____

N: ______________________________

S: ______________________________

____

---

8. A Mäoris tribe of New Zealand built canoes that were 117 feet long. Between 68 and 71 crew members were needed to paddle one of these canoes. About how many crew members were needed to paddle in 5 separate Mäoris canoes?

WORK SPACE

T: ______________________________

I: ______________________________

____

N: ______________________________

S: ______________________________

____

9. Thomas Edison spent 60 years creating and patenting his inventions. He patented between 1,000 and 1,300 inventions in total. About how many of Thomas Edison's inventions were patented each year?

WORK SPACE

T: ____________________

I: ____________________

____

N: ____________________

S: ____________________

____

10. Saffron is one of the most expensive spices in the world. It takes 1 acre of crocus plants to make just 10 pounds of this spice. About how many acres would be needed to produce 220 pounds?

WORK SPACE

T: ____________________

I: ____________________

____

N: ____________________

S: ____________________

____

Estimating Multiplication and Division: Take the Challenge

Make a list of the multiplication key words you know.

____
____
____
____
____
____

Make a list of the division key words you know.

____
____
____
____
____
____

Remember to look for and circle these words in the problems below. Draw pictures, cross out extra information, and use TINS to estimate the best answer. Think about each solution sentence—does it seem reasonable?

---

1. The tongue of one blue whale is as heavy as 10 human beings. If one person weighs between 150 and 165 pounds, estimate the weight of a blue whale's tongue.

WORK SPACE

Thought: ______________________

Information: ______________________

____

Number Sentence: ______________________

Solution Sentence: ______________________

____

2. Stacey was told by her dentist that each human tooth contains up to 50 miles of canals. About how many miles of canals are in 32 teeth?

WORK SPACE

T: ______________________________

I: ______________________________

____

N: ______________________________

S: ______________________________

____

3. Between 1,100 and 1,400 pictures are on display at Colonel Brassbutton's art gallery. Half of these pictures are predicted to sell immediately. Estimate how many are predicted to sell right away.

WORK SPACE

T: ______________________________

I: ______________________________

____

N: ______________________________

S: ______________________________

____

4. Mr. Boyton reports that in New York City more than 190 people pick up the telephone receiver every second. About how many people pick up the phone in New York in 16 seconds?

WORK SPACE

T: ______________________________

I: ______________________________

____

N: ______________________________

S: ______________________________

____

5. A pygmy marmoset monkey from the Amazon rain forest weighs between 3 and 5 ounces. When it is fully grown, this tiny monkey is only 4 or 5 inches tall. Estimate the weight of twelve of these pygmy monkeys.

WORK SPACE

T: ______________________________

I: ______________________________

____

N: ______________________________

S: ______________________________

____

6. Betty works as a cashier between 59 and 63 hours every week. There are 52 weeks in one year. About how many hours will Betty have worked after one year?

WORK SPACE

T: ______________________________

I: ______________________________

____

N: ______________________________

S: ______________________________

____

7. All four lanes on Route 1 were backed up for 5 miles. Six hundred and fifty-one cars were stopped. Estimate the number of cars that were waiting in each lane.

WORK SPACE

T: ______________________________

I: ______________________________

____

N: ______________________________

S: ______________________________

____

8. Pablo Picasso created many works of art. He created an average of 5 works every week for 75 years. About how many works did Picasso produce in 52 weeks?

WORK SPACE

T: ____________________

I: ____________________

____

N: ____________________

S: ____________________

____

9. Dexter's Dairy bottles between 1,990 and 2,015 quarts of pasteurized milk in one day. About how many quarts will Dexter's Dairy produce after 10 days?

WORK SPACE

T: ____________________

I: ____________________

____

N: ____________________

S: ____________________

____

10. Hattie's parrot speaks between 4,550 and 4,713 words in one day. What is a good estimate of how many words Hattie's parrot might speak in 14 days?

WORK SPACE

T: ____________________

I: ____________________

____

N: ____________________

S: ____________________

____

11. A large fountain at Maple Beach shoots water 20 feet into the air and makes three pools of water on the pavement below. Fifty-seven people ran into the pools. If an equal number of people ran into each pool, estimate how many people were in each pool.

WORK SPACE

T: ______________________________

I: ______________________________

____

N: ______________________________

S: ______________________________

____

12. Deena Finch, real estate tycoon, sold 6 houses in one month for similar prices. The total selling price for all the houses was $859,000. Estimate the cost of only one house.

WORK SPACE

T: ______________________________

I: ______________________________

____

N: ______________________________

S: ______________________________

____

13. In 1927, Charles Lindbergh flew his plane, *The Spirit of St. Louis,* from New York to Paris without stopping to refuel. His flight won him a prize of $25,000. The flight took 33.5 hours and covered between 3,400 and 3,610 miles. Estimate the number of miles Lindbergh traveled in one hour.

WORK SPACE

T: ______________________________

I: ______________________________

____

N: ______________________________

S: ______________________________

____

14. Noah planted 34 raspberry bushes in 5 rows. Estimate the number of bushes in each row.

WORK SPACE

T: ____________________

I: ____________________

____

N: ____________________

S: ____________________

____

---

15. Margaret Bourke-White took between 279 and 291 photographs for a famous magazine. If she worked for the magazine for 20 years, estimate the number of photographs Bourke-White took in one year.

WORK SPACE

T: ____________________

I: ____________________

____

N: ____________________

S: ____________________

____

---

16. Forty-three members of the Knickerbocker Club asked a total of 1,020 people to sponsor them in a walk for charity. 771 people agreed to sponsor members. Estimate the number of sponsors each member obtained.

WORK SPACE

T: ____________________

I: ____________________

____

N: ____________________

S: ____________________

____

17. Rick baked 23 pumpkin pies on Friday. Nine restaurants requested his pies. Estimate the number of pies Rick was able to give each restaurant on Friday.

WORK SPACE

T: ______________________________

I: ______________________________

____

N: ______________________________

S: ______________________________

____

18. At the camera club meeting, Professor Patel presented 409 slides in 24 minutes. About how many slides did she present in one minute?

WORK SPACE

T: ______________________________

I: ______________________________

____

N: ______________________________

S: ______________________________

____

19. During Billy's trip to Mount Washington in New Hampshire, he traveled between 48 and 52 miles. Billy counted 4,222 telephone poles along the way. Estimate the number of poles Billy counted per mile.

WORK SPACE

T: ______________________________

I: ______________________________

____

N: ______________________________

S: ______________________________

____

20. The weather forecaster on Channel 3 reports that one thundercloud can contain 100,000 tons of water. Eighteen thunderclouds passed over Lakeshire in June. About how many tons of water were contained in those thunderclouds?

WORK SPACE

T: ______________________________

I: ______________________________

____

N: ______________________________

S: ______________________________

____

Write Your Own I

Use the information provided to write your own multiplication or division word problems. Then use TINS to solve each problem. Check that your answers seem reasonable. Challenge your friends to estimate the answers to some of the problems you create!

Example: Aleeyah and Bernard, two very fast hikers, can travel one mile in 6 minutes. They hike uphill for 48 minutes.

Question: Aleeyah and Bernard hike one mile in 6 minutes. Estimate the number of minutes it would take them to cover 48 miles. ?

Thought: x

Information: 6 minutes for 1 mile, 48 miles

Number Sentence: 6 x 50 =

Solution Sentence: It will take the hikers about 300 minutes to travel 48 miles.

WORK SPACE

5:00

1 mile

300:00

50 miles

---

1. There are eighteen apple trees in the grove. Thirty apples are found on one tree.

Question: ______________________________ ?

Thought: ______________________________

Information: ______________________________

Number Sentence: ______________________________

Solution Sentence: ______________________________

WORK SPACE

2. It usually takes 38 minutes to wash one dog. Six dogs arrived.

WORK SPACE

Question: ____

____

____?

T: ____

I: ____

____

N: ____

S: ____

____

---

3. There are two lifeguards on duty. There are eleven miles of white sand on the beach.

WORK SPACE

Question: ____

____

____?

T: ____

I: ____

____

N: ____

S: ____

____

4. The roller coaster has 82 seats. Each roller coaster car has between 1 and 3 seats in it.

WORK SPACE

Question: ______________________________

____

______________________________?

T: ______________________________

I: ______________________________

____

N: ______________________________

S: ______________________________

____

---

5. The race attracted 24 sailboats. Each boat has a crew of between 3 and 5 sailors.

WORK SPACE

Question: ______________________________

____

______________________________?

T: ______________________________

I: ______________________________

____

N: ______________________________

S: ______________________________

____

Write Your Own II

Write five new multiplication and division word problems using your own information. Remember to draw a picture, circle key words, and cross out your extra information. Then use TINS to estimate a reasonable solution. Be creative!

1. ______________________________

____

______________________________?

WORK SPACE

Thought: ______________________________

Information: ______________________________

____

Number Sentence: ______________________________

Solution Sentence: ______________________________

____

---

2. ______________________________

____

______________________________?

WORK SPACE

T: ______________________________

I: ______________________________

____

N: ______________________________

S: ______________________________

____

3. ______________________________

____

______________________________?

T: ______________________________

I: ______________________________

____

N: ______________________________

S: ______________________________

____

WORK SPACE

4. ______________________________

____

______________________________?

T: ______________________________

I: ______________________________

____

N: ______________________________

S: ______________________________

____

WORK SPACE

5. ______________________________

____

______________________________?

T: ______________________________

I: ______________________________

____

N: ______________________________

S: ______________________________

____

WORK SPACE

Multiplication and Division Mixed Review

Use TINS to solve these word problems. Remember to circle key words, draw pictures, and cross out extra information. Check your solutions. Are they reasonable?

1. Over half of the scientists at the annual convention believe that the moon is still wobbling from a colossal meteorite impact 800 years ago. If there were 495 scientists attending the convention, about how many scientists believe this theory?

WORK SPACE

Thought: ____________________

Information: ____________________

____

Number Sentence: ____________________

Solution Sentence: ____________________

____

---

2. Judge Trumball's truck can travel 16.4 miles on one gallon of gasoline. About how much gasoline will the judge need for a 316-mile trip?

WORK SPACE

T: ____________________

I: ____________________

____

N: ____________________

S: ____________________

____

3. Cynthia watched 12 passenger trains pass by her house when she was home with the flu. She recorded between 59 and 63 cars in all. The westbound train arrives every two hours. Estimate the number of cars in each passing train.

WORK SPACE

T: ______________________________

I: ______________________________

____

N: ______________________________

S: ______________________________

____

4. Regina interviewed 30 baby-sitters over the phone. If each interview lasted between 17 and 23 minutes, about how long did Regina talk on the phone?

WORK SPACE

T: ______________________________

I: ______________________________

____

N: ______________________________

S: ______________________________

____

5. The National Portrait Gallery in Washington, D.C., has 5 times as many pieces of art as it did in 1970. It now has between 4,325 and 4,500 pieces. About how many art pieces did the National Portrait Gallery have in 1970?

WORK SPACE

T: ______________________________

I: ______________________________

____

N: ______________________________

S: ______________________________

____

6. Amelia Earhart was the first woman to fly solo over the Atlantic Ocean. Her trip covered between 2,001 and 2,026 miles in 15 hours. About how many miles did Amelia Earhart fly in 1 hour?

WORK SPACE

T: ______________________________

I: ______________________________

____

N: ______________________________

S: ______________________________

____

7. The town of Sunnydale has a population of 431. It is estimated that Sunnydale's population will expand to 5 times its size in the next 2 years. After 2 years, what will be the estimated population of Sunnydale?

WORK SPACE

T: ______________________________

I: ______________________________

____

N: ______________________________

S: ______________________________

____

8. Louisa May Alcott is one of the first best-selling novelists in America. Her book *Little Women* sold between 34,000 and 38,000 copies in 1869. If the same number of copies were sold each month, about how many copies were sold in 30 days?

WORK SPACE

T: ______________________________

I: ______________________________

____

N: ______________________________

S: ______________________________

____

9. The Great Pyramid at Giza is estimated to be 480 feet, 11 inches high. It took between 2,000,000 and 2,500,000 stone blocks and 20 years to build. Estimate the number of blocks that were used in one year.

WORK SPACE

T: ______________________________

I: ______________________________

____

N: ______________________________

S: ______________________________

____

10. Nina's sticker album has 9 pages. Each page contains 6 stickers. Estimate the number of stickers in Nina's album.

WORK SPACE

T: ______________________________

I: ______________________________

____

N: ______________________________

S: ______________________________

____

11. Jerome counted 621 sheets in one package of printing paper. Estimate the number of sheets Jerome would find in 16 packages of paper.

WORK SPACE

T: ______________________________

I: ______________________________

____

N: ______________________________

S: ______________________________

____

12. Rudy is a philatelist, or a stamp collector, and has collected more than 868 stamps. His son Ernest has 6 sheets of rare stamps with 56 stamps on each sheet. Estimate the number of stamps Ernest has altogether.

WORK SPACE

T: ____________________

I: ____________________

____

N: ____________________

S: ____________________

____

13. I.M. Pei is the famous architect who designed the Rock & Roll Hall of Fame. The cost of admission to this museum is between $11.50 and $14.98. Estimate how much it will cost 12 people to buy tickets.

WORK SPACE

T: ____________________

I: ____________________

____

N: ____________________

S: ____________________

____

14. Bessie Smith was known as the Empress of the Blues. Her first record, *Down Hearted Blues,* sold between 780,000 and 820,000 copies in 6 months. Estimate the number of records that were sold in one month.

WORK SPACE

T: ____________________

I: ____________________

____

N: ____________________

S: ____________________

____

15. Stylists at Bob's Beauty Salon reported a record 63 appointments on Monday. Half of the customers were new. Estimate the number of new customers.

WORK SPACE

T: ______________________________

I: ______________________________

____

N: ______________________________

S: ______________________________

____

16. The U.S. Pentagon covers more land area than any building in the world. It has 6.5 million square feet of office space that covers 5 floors. Estimate the number of square feet on each floor.

WORK SPACE

T: ______________________________

I: ______________________________

____

N: ______________________________

S: ______________________________

____

17. Susan's bulldog, Aristotle, weighs 3 times as much as Joan's poodle, Socrates. If Socrates weighs between 17 and 21 pounds, about how much does Aristotle weigh?

WORK SPACE

T: ______________________________

I: ______________________________

____

N: ______________________________

S: ______________________________

____

18. The battleship U.S.S. *New Jersey* is reported to be 3 times as long as an American football field. The battleship measures 887 feet. Estimate the length, in feet, of a football field.

WORK SPACE

T: ______________________________

I: ______________________________

____

N: ______________________________

S: ______________________________

____

19. In Ruby's book, Washington Irving's tale of "Rip Van Winkle" is 17 pages long. "The Legend of Sleepy Hollow" is twice as long. About how many pages is "The Legend of Sleepy Hollow"?

WORK SPACE

T: ______________________________

I: ______________________________

____

N: ______________________________

S: ______________________________

____

WORK SPACE

20. If 1,760 yards are equal in length to 1 mile, estimate how many yards are in half of a mile.

T: ______________________________

I: ______________________________

____

N: ______________________________

S: ______________________________

____

Explain

Use TINS to solve each multiplication or division word problem. Then write at least 2 sentences explaining why your estimate is reasonable.

Example: Drew picked 31 ripe watermelons from his patch. He sold the watermelons to three different restaurants for ~~$2.75~~ each. Estimate how many watermelons went to each restaurant.

WORK SPACE

Thought: ÷

Information: 31 watermelons, 3 restaurants

Number Sentence: 30 ÷ 3 =

Solution Sentence: Drew sold about 10 watermelons to each restaurant.

Explanation: ______

---

1. Mrs. Martinez would like to spend $18 on Chinese food. She selects six appetizers priced between $0.52 and $2.98. Will $18 be enough money for all six appetizers?

WORK SPACE

Thought: ______

Information: ______

Number Sentence: ______

Solution Sentence: ______

Explanation: ______

2. In October, the Halloween haunted house is open 4 nights a week. If 589 people take the tour in one week, about how many people tour the house in one night?

WORK SPACE

T: ____________________

I: ____________________

____

N: ____________________

S: ____________________

____

Explanation: ____________________

____

____

3. The ballet company held auditions for *Swan Lake*. Eighty-three people arrived for the audition. If half of the dancers were called back, about how many people had a second audition?

WORK SPACE

T: ____________________

I: ____________________

____

N: ____________________

S: ____________________

____

Explanation: ____________________

____

____

Final Mixed Review

Use TINS to estimate the solution to these word problems. You'll need to use addition, subtraction, multiplication, and division. Remember to circle key words, draw pictures, and cross out extra information.

1. Arthur became lost while driving north on Highway 95. His trip was supposed to cover 28 miles. If he drove between 8 and 10 extra miles, how many miles did Arthur actually drive?

WORK SPACE

Thought: ______________________________

Information: ______________________________

____

Number Sentence: ______________________________

Solution Sentence: ______________________________

____

---

2. Leonardo da Vinci began painting the *Mona Lisa* in 1503 and finished in 1506. If he used between 49 and 58 brushes in one year, estimate how many brushes he used in four years.

WORK SPACE

T: ______________________________

I: ______________________________

____

N: ______________________________

S: ______________________________

____

3. A chameleon measures between 5 and 7 inches long and has a 12-inch tongue. About how much longer is the chameleon's tongue than its body?

WORK SPACE

T: ______________________________

I: ______________________________

____

N: ______________________________

S: ______________________________

____

4. The woolly mammoth is reported to have stood between 13 and 15 feet high, with tusks that were 13 feet long. Elephants today usually grow to be 10 feet tall. About how much taller was the woolly mammoth than today's elephants?

WORK SPACE

T: ______________________________

I: ______________________________

____

N: ______________________________

S: ______________________________

____

5. It takes an oyster five years to make an average-sized pearl. A very large pearl takes between 8 and 10 years. About how many more years does it take an oyster to make a very large pearl?

WORK SPACE

T: ______________________________

I: ______________________________

____

N: ______________________________

S: ______________________________

____

6. It took 28 minutes for Irina to ride her motorcycle to the railroad station. The trip home took her twice as long. About how many minutes did it take for Irina to ride home?

WORK SPACE

T: ______________________________

I: ______________________________

____

N: ______________________________

S: ______________________________

____

7. Kumi's report stated that most dogs are fully grown after 2.0 years, most cats after 1.5 years, and most horses after 4.5 years. About how many years does it take for all three animals to become fully grown?

WORK SPACE

T: ______________________________

I: ______________________________

____

N: ______________________________

S: ______________________________

____

8. Hector has $20. If he spends $3.55 at the florist and $9.99 at the pharmacy, will he have enough money for a five-dollar lunch?

WORK SPACE

T: ______________________________

I: ______________________________

____

N: ______________________________

S: ______________________________

____

9. Elliot made two big salads for a party on Monday. He used 5 heads of lettuce, two dozen tomatoes, spices, and 138 large croutons in all. About how many croutons did Elliot put in each salad bowl?

WORK SPACE

T: ____________________

I: ____________________

____

N: ____________________

S: ____________________

____

10. Red stars can have a temperature of 4,140 degrees Fahrenheit. Blue stars are usually 5 times hotter than red stars. Give an estimate of the temperature of a blue star.

WORK SPACE

T: ____________________

I: ____________________

____

N: ____________________

S: ____________________

____

11. A typical eyebrow has between 480 and 550 hairs. Estimate the number of hairs that are on both of your eyebrows.

WORK SPACE

T: ____________________

I: ____________________

____

N: ____________________

S: ____________________

____

12. In 23 years, the famous fictional detective Sherlock Holmes appeared in over 40 of Arthur Conan Doyle's stories. Estimate the number of Sherlock Holmes stories Mr. Doyle wrote in one year.

WORK SPACE

T: ____________________

I: ____________________

____

N: ____________________

S: ____________________

____

13. *Cleopatra's Needles,* two four-sided granite columns engraved with hieroglyphics, were built in Egypt 3,500 years ago. Egypt gave one of the columns to New York City about 119 years ago. About how long was *Cleopatra's Needle* in Egypt before it was moved to New York?

WORK SPACE

T: ____________________

I: ____________________

____

N: ____________________

S: ____________________

____

14. A swarm of 50,000 locusts have been known to eat between 79,000 and 90,000 tons of crops in one day. At this rate, about how many tons of crops would be eaten after 3 days?

WORK SPACE

T: ____________________

I: ____________________

____

N: ____________________

S: ____________________

____

15. Bristlecone pine trees located in the White Mountains of northern California are thought to be between 4,300 and 4,800 years old. Park rangers believe they could live for another 650 years. Estimate the expected life span of the bristlecone pine.

WORK SPACE

T: ____________________

I: ____________________

____

N: ____________________

S: ____________________

____

---

16. The Museum of Natural History at the Smithsonian Institute has two aquariums at its entrance. One is for cold-water species and the other is for tropical species. If the tanks contain 5,861 gallons of water in all, estimate the number of gallons in one tank.

WORK SPACE

T: ____________________

I: ____________________

____

N: ____________________

S: ____________________

____

---

17. Hummingbirds are known to travel between 55 and 66 miles in one hour. Estimate how far, in miles, a hummingbird can travel in three hours.

WORK SPACE

T: ____________________

I: ____________________

____

N: ____________________

S: ____________________

____

18. Jerzy reports that his school library contains 25,159 books, 1,788 journals, and 4,589 audio and video tapes. About how many materials are there in total in Jerzy's school library?

WORK SPACE

T: ______________________________

I: ______________________________

____

N: ______________________________

S: ______________________________

____

19. Mrs. Johnson bought 3 hairbrushes. Each brush contains 12 rows of bristles. If the total number of bristles on one brush is 582, estimate the number of bristles in one row.

WORK SPACE

T: ______________________________

I: ______________________________

____

N: ______________________________

S: ______________________________

____

20. The wax museum has 42 exhibits representing famous people and events. Between 180 and 210 historical figures are shown in all. About how many historical figures are represented in each exhibit?

WORK SPACE

T: ______________________________

I: ______________________________

____

N: ______________________________

S: ______________________________

____

21. A millennium is equal to 100 decades. One decade is equal to 10 years. If one year contains 365 days, about how many days are in one decade?

WORK SPACE

T: ______________________________

I: ______________________________

____

N: ______________________________

S: ______________________________

____

22. The lyrics of "The Star-Spangled Banner" were written during the War of 1812. It was adopted as the U.S. national anthem in 1931. Estimate how many years it took for this song to become the national anthem.

WORK SPACE

T: ______________________________

I: ______________________________

____

N: ______________________________

S: ______________________________

____

23. Crocodiles swallow rocks to balance their tails while they swim. Each crocodile at the zoo swallowed between 35 and 40 rocks. If the zoo has 3 crocodiles, about how many rocks have the crocodiles swallowed in total?

WORK SPACE

T: ______________________________

I: ______________________________

____

N: ______________________________

S: ______________________________

____

24. Mr. Leonard weighs 9 times more than his dog, Kiki. If Kiki weighs between 19 and 23 pounds, estimate how much Mr. Leonard weighs.

WORK SPACE

T: ______________________________

I: ______________________________

____

N: ______________________________

S: ______________________________

____

25. Claudia's magazine has 247 pages of advertisements. If her magazine has 398 pages, how many pages do not have advertisements?

WORK SPACE

T: ______________________________

I: ______________________________

____

N: ______________________________

S: ______________________________

____

26. Larissa bought 178 beads. She plans to use all of the beads to make 9 necklaces. Estimate the number of beads on each of the necklaces Larissa makes.

WORK SPACE

T: ______________________________

I: ______________________________

____

N: ______________________________

S: ______________________________

____

27. Omar swam 48 laps in the indoor pool. If he spent 120 minutes in the pool, about how many minutes did it take Omar to swim one lap?

WORK SPACE

T: ______________________________

I: ______________________________

____

N: ______________________________

S: ______________________________

____

28. Jackie spent 45 minutes stretching her hamstrings. She did 12 different stretching exercises. Estimate how much time Jackie spent on each exercise.

WORK SPACE

T: ______________________________

I: ______________________________

____

N: ______________________________

S: ______________________________

____

29. Maura spent $599 on ski equipment. Since the skis were on sale, she saved $210. Give an estimate of the original cost of Maura's equipment.

WORK SPACE

T: ______________________________

I: ______________________________

____

N: ______________________________

S: ______________________________

____

30. Truffles, expensive Italian mushrooms, cost $195 an ounce at the gourmet shop. Mr. Rios bought 5 ounces. Estimate how much money Mr. Rios paid for the truffles in all.

WORK SPACE

T: ____________________

I: ____________________

____

N: ____________________

S: ____________________

____

Estimating Word Problems Using Graphs and Charts

These exercises use graphs and charts to organize important information. There are many different types of graphs. This section uses bar graphs and pictographs. You will see that graphs and charts are great tools for recording your estimates. For these word problems, you will need to search

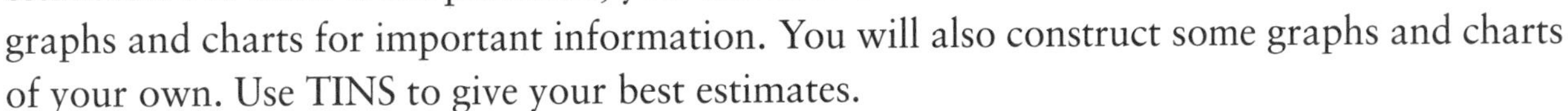

graphs and charts for important information. You will also construct some graphs and charts of your own. Use TINS to give your best estimates.

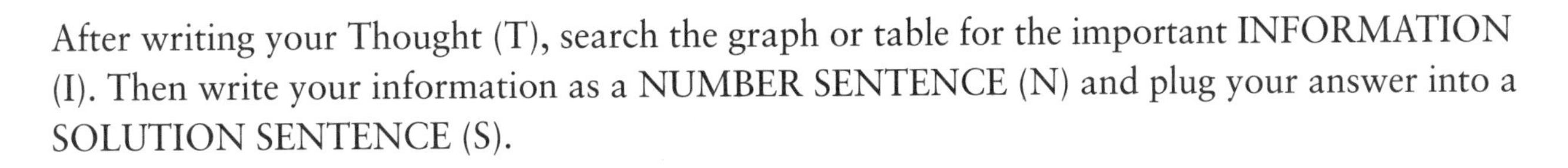

After writing your Thought (T), search the graph or table for the important INFORMATION (I). Then write your information as a NUMBER SENTENCE (N) and plug your answer into a SOLUTION SENTENCE (S).

Example: The pictograph shows the number of goals Olympia scored in her last five soccer games.

Estimate the number of goals Olympia scored in all five soccer games.

Thought: +

Information: Week 1: 9, Week 2: 8, Week 3: 14, Week 4: 17, Week 5: 14

Number Sentence: 10 + 10 + 10 + 20 + 10

Solution Sentence: Olympia scored about 60 goals in all.

WORK SPACE

Week 1 Week 2 Week 3 Week 4 Week 5

Try It Out

Use TINS to estimate the best solutions to these word problems. For some problems, you will need to retrieve important information from a graph or chart. For others, you will need to create your own graph or chart from the important information in the problem.

This graph shows pets owned by students at Harrison Elementary School. Each student owns only one of the pets in the graph.

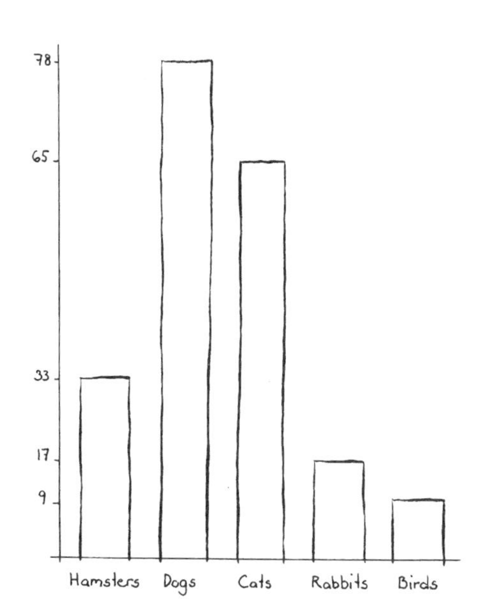

1. About how many more students at Harrison Elementary School have dogs than rabbits?

Thought: ______________________________

Information: ______________________________

____

Number Sentence: ______________________________

Solution Sentence: ______________________________

____

2. What is a good estimate for the total number of students who have a rabbit, a bird, or a cat?

WORK SPACE

T: ______________________________

I: ______________________________

____

N: ______________________________

S: ______________________________

____

The graph at the right shows the weather conditions for the month of January in Portland, Maine.

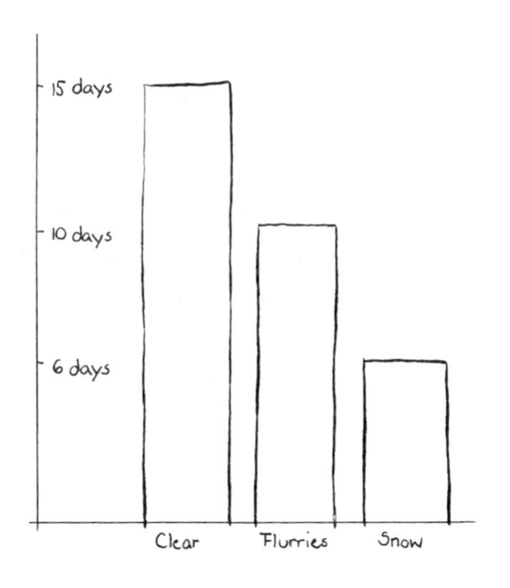

3. What is a good estimate for the total number of days with snow or snow flurries for the month of January?

WORK SPACE

T: ______________________

I: ______________________

____

N: ______________________

S: ______________________

____

4. Half of the clear days in Maine were also sunny. Estimate how many sunny days there were in January.

WORK SPACE

T: ______________________

I: ______________________

____

N: ______________________

S: ______________________

____

Composers use musical notation when they write music. Clara used these symbols to write a song for the class play.

musical notes	number of beats
whole notes	4
half notes	2
quarter notes	1
eighth notes	1/2

5. If Clara used only 28 half notes in her composition, about how many beats will there be in her song?

WORK SPACE

T: ______________________________

I: ______________________________

____

N: ______________________________

S: ______________________________

____

6. Clara wants to add 12 extra beats to her song using only whole notes. How many whole notes will she need to add?

WORK SPACE

T: ______________________________

I: ______________________________

____

N: ______________________________

S: ______________________________

____

Use the information from the chart below to create a bar graph that shows the number of pencils sold at the school store during each term. Use TINS to estimate the solution to each problem. Remember to label your graph.

Number of pencils sold

	At least	At most
1st term	40	45
2nd term	5	10
3rd term	15	20
4th term	30	35

7. Estimate how many more pencils were bought in the first term than in the second term.

WORK SPACE

T: ____________________

I: ____________________

____

N: ____________________

S: ____________________

____

8. Why do you think more pencils are sold in the first term of school than in the second term? If you were manager, how would you stock the school store?

____

____

____

____

The following table shows the number of awards won by students at 97th Street School from 1997 to 2000. Draw a picture graph to show this information.

Year	Number of awards
1997	3
1998	6
1999	9
2000	12

9. What is a good estimate for the total number of awards won during all four of the years shown?

WORK SPACE

T: ______________________________

I: ______________________________

____

N: ______________________________

S: ______________________________

____

10. If this pattern continues, how many awards would you expect the school to win next year? Explain your reasoning.

____

____

____

____

In his sixth-grade class, Mr. Ortiz conducted a survey about his students' favorite kinds of pizza. Create a graph showing the students' votes.

Sausage: 10 students

Pepperoni: 5 students

Cheese: 13 students

Veggie: 4 students

11. What is a good estimate for the total number of students who prefer veggie or cheese pizza?

WORK SPACE

Thought: ______________________________

Information: ______________________________

____

Number Sentence: ______________________________

Solution Sentence: ______________________________

____

12. Mr. Ortiz wants to order 2 large single-topping pizzas for his class to thank them for all of their hard work. What kinds of toppings do you think he should order? Explain your reasoning.

____

____

____

____

Kasey trained for her school track meet for four weeks. She made a list showing the number of miles she ran each week.

Week 1	11–14 miles
Week 2	15–18 miles
Week 3	19–22 miles
Week 4	23–26 miles

13. What is a good estimate for the total number of miles Kasey ran during her four weeks of training for her school track meet?

WORK SPACE

T: ____________________

I: ____________________

____

N: ____________________

S: ____________________

____

14. If she continues training at this rate, how long do you think it will be before she can run 30 miles? Explain your reasoning.

____

____

____

____

This list shows the price of admission to Highland Cinema for a family of four during the past five years:

1996	$20
1997	$25
1998	$30
1999	$35
2000	$40

15. If a family of four went to three movies in 1999 what is a good estimate if how much money they would have spent on movie tickets?

WORK SPACE

T: ______________________________

I: ______________________________

____

N: ______________________________

S: ______________________________

____

16. What is a good estimate of the total amount of money a family of four would have spent on movie tickets if they went to a movie once a year during the past five years?

WORK SPACE

T: ______________________________

I: ______________________________

____

N: ______________________________

S: ______________________________

____

17. If this pattern continues, how much would you expect a family of four to spend on tickets for a movie in 2001?

____

____

____

Final Estimation Review

Use everything you have learned about TINS to give your best estimates for these word problems.

1. Keisha has a button collection containing 435 buttons. During her summer vacation she collected 234 additional buttons. About how many buttons does Keisha have now?

WORK SPACE

Thought: ______________________________

Information: ______________________________

____

Number Sentence: ______________________________

Solution Sentence: ______________________________

____

---

2. Aren and Steve have 786 baseball cards between them. They sold 143 baseball cards at a card show. What is a good estimate of how many baseball cards Aren and Steve have left?

WORK SPACE

T: ______________________________

I: ______________________________

____

N: ______________________________

S: ______________________________

____

Round each number to the nearest ten.

3. 13 ________ **5.** 45 ________ **7.** 67 ________

4. 85 ________ **6.** 22 ________ **8.** 29 ________

Round each number to the nearest hundred.

9. 435 ________ **11.** 678 ________ **13.** 550 ________

10. 123 ________ **12.** 420 ________ **14.** 679 ________

Round each number to the nearest thousand.

15. 1,001 ________ **17.** 5,500 ________ **19.** 4,897 ________

16. 7,550 ________ **18.** 2,222 ________ **20.** 5,575 ________

The following list shows the number of granola bars consumed by Lindsey's fourth grade class last week.

WORK SPACE

Monday	18
Tuesday	21
Wednesday	27
Thursday	6
Friday	15

21. According to the list, about hcw many granola bars did Lindsey's class eat last week?

T: ________________________________

I: ________________________________

____

N: ________________________________

S: ________________________________

____

Research

1. Look in your local newspaper or search the Internet to find airline fares. Research how much it would cost for someone to fly to Florida from where you live.

WORK SPACE

---

2. Look back at the first example in this book. Does the price the Howard family paid for their airline tickets seem reasonable? Explain your reasoning.

WORK SPACE

You can write the key words that you know in each operation sign.
Then cut out the signs and put them on your desk or in your math folder.

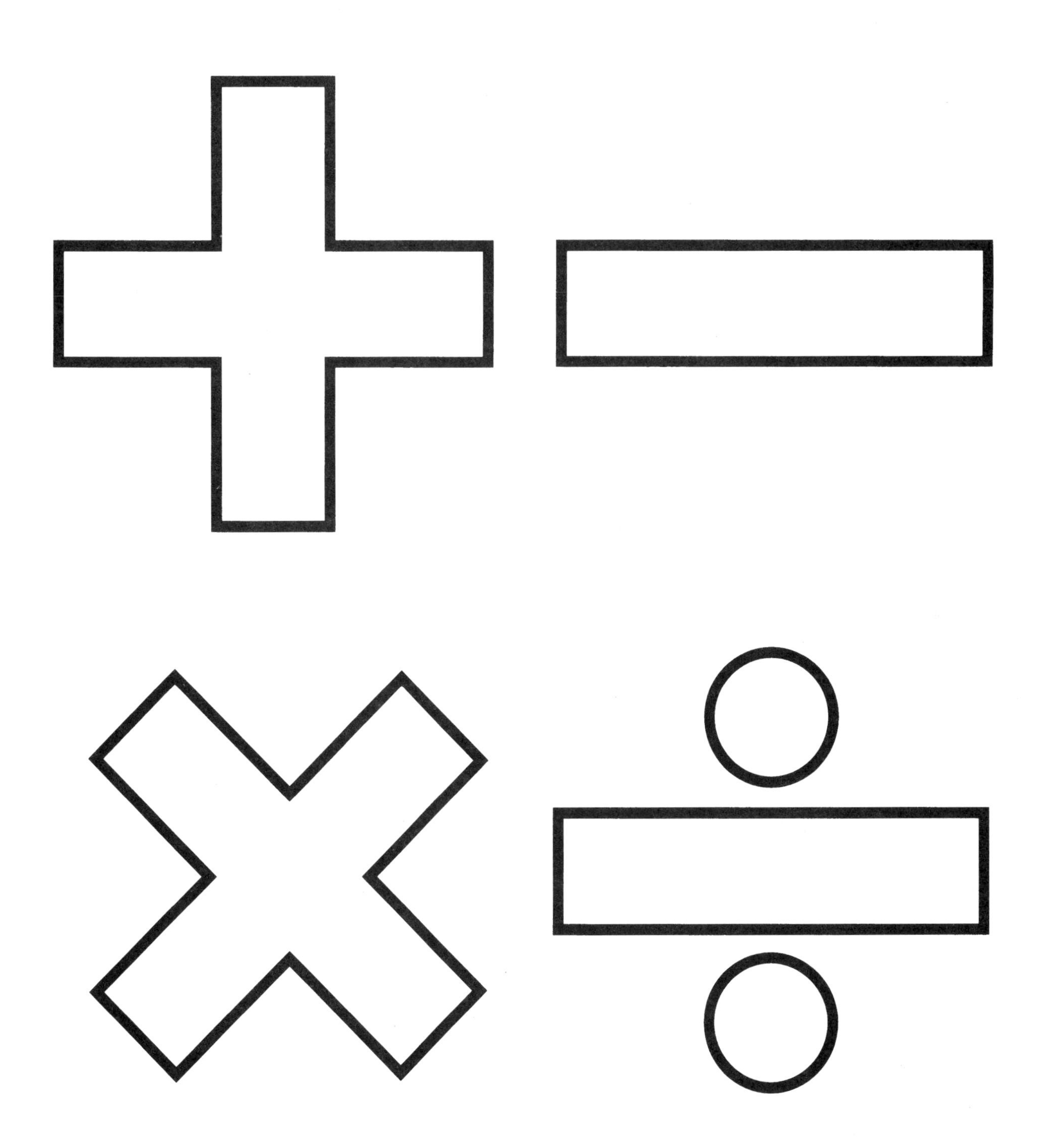